Level C

To the Student

This book has exciting articles for you to read and enjoy. They tell about real-life adventures, unusual animals, famous people, interesting places, and important events.

There are questions after each article to help you think about what you have read. The last question will give you a chance to write about the article.

Comprehension means "understanding." Good readers comprehend what they read. You can become a better reader and writer as you go through this book and focus on understanding.

 Continental Press

Elizabethtown, PA 17022

Credits

Editorial Development: Matt Baker, Beth Spencer

Editorial Support: Joyce Ober, Anthony Moore

Cover and Interior Design: Joan Herring

Illustrators: Pages 20, 21; 48, 49 Rob Williams; Pages 46, 47; 56, 57; 58, 59; 66, 67; 82, 83; 94, 95 Margaret Lindmark

Photo Credits: Front cover: *Bald eagle, saguaro cactus, giraffes:* www.photos.com; *clownfish:* www.istockphoto.com/redtwiggy; *Mt. Rushmore:* www.istockphoto.com/megasquib; *open book:* www.istockphoto.com/mstay; Pages 4, 5: www.photos.com; Pages 6, 7: www.istockphoto.com; Pages 8, 9: www.photos.com; Pages 10, 11: www.whitehouse.gov; Pages 12, 13: www.photos.com; Pages 14, 15: www.istockphoto.com/drbueller; Pages 16, 17: www.photos.com; Pages 18, 19: www.uscourts.gov; Pages 22, 23: www.photos.com; Pages 24, 25: www.photos.com; Pages 26, 27: www.istockphoto.com; Pages 28, 29: www.istockphoto.com; Pages 30, 31: www.photos.com; Pages 32, 33: www.photos.com; Pages 34, 35: www.photos.com; Pages 36, 37: www.photos.com; Pages 38, 39: NASA; Pages 40, 41: NASA/JPL/Space Science Institute; Pages 42, 43: www.photos.com; Pages 44, 45: NOAA Photo Library; Pages 50, 51: www.photos.com; Pages 52, 53: www.photos.com; Pages 54, 55: Library of Congress Prints and Photographs Division, LC-GLB23-1356DLC; Pages 60, 61: www.photos.com; Pages 62, 63: www.wikipedia.org; Pages 64, 65: www.photos.com; Pages 68, 69: www.photos.com; Pages 70, 71: Library of Congress Prints and Photographs Division, LC-USZ62-15887; Pages 72, 73: www.photos.com; Pages 74, 75: www.photos.com; Pages 76, 77: www.photos.com; Pages 78, 79: www.istockphoto.com/matt.scherf; Pages 80, 81: www.photos.com; Pages 84, 85: www.istockphoto.com/jeu; Pages 86, 87: www.wikipedia.org; Pages 88, 89: www.photos.com; Pages 90, 91: www.wikipedia.org; Pages 92, 93: www.photos.com

ISBN 978-0-8454-1682-2

Contents

How do people breathe?

1   Most of the time, you don't think about breathing. Air moves in and out of your lungs 15 to 25 times every minute. But why do you breathe? And what happens in your body when you breathe?

2   People breathe to take in good air and get rid of bad air. All the cells in the human body need a gas called oxygen. And cells need to get rid of a gas called carbon dioxide.

3   How does this happen? Air enters your nose and mouth. It goes down a tube called the trachea (TRAY•kee•uh) into two tubes. One tube goes into each lung. Your lungs are two sacs that act like sponges. Inside each lung, the tubes divide into smaller tubes. At the end of the tubes are millions of tiny sacs called alveoli (al•VEE•uh•ly). This is where your blood receives good air and unloads bad air.

4   The air you breathe is not always clean. Sticky areas of your nose, trachea, and lungs trap dirt and germs. But your lungs have little hairs called cilia (SIL•ee•uh). They act like tiny brooms to push the dirt and germs out of your lungs.

Correct.

Circle the right answer for questions 1–5. Write your answer to question 6 on a blank piece of paper.

1. The air people breathe moves in and out of the lungs _____ times per minute.
   A 5 to 10
   B 15 to 25
   C 25 to 50
   D 35 to 65

2. Which word in paragraph 3 means "comes in"?
   A goes
   B unloads
   C enters
   D receives

3. Which paragraph tells about the purpose of breathing?
   A 1
   B 2
   C 3
   D 4

4. After air goes down your trachea, the air next enters _____.
   A your nose and mouth
   B millions of tiny sacs
   C your lungs
   D two tubes

5. The article does not say, but you can decide that the cilia _____.
   A help people stay healthy
   B pass oxygen to the blood
   C get rid of carbon dioxide
   D make the lungs wider

BONUS

6. Think of a time when you had trouble breathing. What helped you breathe better?

What is the "Forehead of the Sky"?

1   Mount Everest is the highest mountain on Earth. The mountain is in central Asia. Some Asian people call the mountain the "Forehead of the Sky."

2   It is hard to climb Mount Everest. The mountain is steep and rocky. The weather is cold and windy. Often there are fierce storms. Sometimes an avalanche crashes down the mountain. The hike down can be just as hard as going up.

3   The mountain is so high that the air is thin. It is hard to breathe. A climber must move slowly near the mountain's top. The climber takes six or eight breaths before each tiny step. Some climbers get mountain sickness. Their brains do not get enough oxygen. The climbers feel sick and confused. Most climbers take bottles of oxygen to help them breathe.

4   Many people have tried to climb Mount Everest. But not many have reached the top. In 1953, Edmund Hillary and Tenzing Norgay were the first climbers to reach the summit. In 2001, the first blind climber made it to the top. Why do people try so hard to climb Mount Everest? Here is what many climbers say: "Because it is there."

Correct

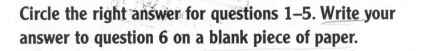

Circle the right answer for questions 1–5. Write your
answer to question 6 on a blank piece of paper.

1. Mount Everest is located in central _____.
   A Asia   C Europe
   B Africa   D America

2. Which word in paragraph 2 means "showing force"?
   A hard   C fierce
   B steep   D rocky

3. A climber takes six or eight breaths before each step because the _____.
   A climber is confused
   B weather is cold
   C storm is fierce
   D air is thin

4. The article does not say, but you can decide that mountain sickness
   is caused by _____.
   A a cold
   B sore legs
   C lack of sleep
   D lack of oxygen

5. *Call* can have the following meanings. Mark the meaning used in
   paragraph 1.
   A to say something in a loud voice
   B to give something a name
   C to send a message
   D to predict

BONUS

6. Would you ever like to climb Mount Everest? Why or why not?

1   Alligators belong to the same animal family as snakes and turtles. Snakes and turtles are quiet. But an alligator is different. It makes its first sound even before it comes out of its egg. These noises tell the mother that it is time to free her babies from the nest.

2   Young alligators sometimes squeak. Grown alligators make other sounds. They hiss when they are angry or afraid. In alligator country, a hiss may mean that an angry alligator is coming at you. Or it may mean that a frightened alligator is slipping into the water to get away.

3   The most common alligator sound is a roar. Alligators often roar on spring evenings. They are looking for a mate. The roar of an alligator is one of the great animal sounds of the world.

4   Alligators can also be quiet. They float without sound in the water. Only their eyes and noses show. Alligators are often quiet in summer and winter. If the weather is too hot or too cold, they fall into a deep sleep.

Circle the right answer for questions 1–5. Write your answer to question 6 on a blank piece of paper.

1. The article does <u>not</u> tell about the _____ of an alligator.
   A   tail
   B   sleep
   C   sounds
   D   mother

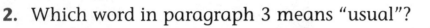

2. Which word in paragraph 3 means "usual"?
   A   roar   C   great
   B   most   D   common

3. Which paragraph tells when alligators are quiet?
   A   1   C   3
   B   2   D   4

4. Alligators hiss when they are _____.
   A   angry
   B   sleeping
   C   caring for babies
   D   looking for a mate

5. The article does not say, but you can decide that alligators _____.
   A   roar throughout the day
   B   only sleep in the summer
   C   do not like very cold temperatures
   D   make the same sounds as babies and adults

BONUS
6. How are alligators like big cats, such as lions and tigers? How are they different?

What is the first lady's job?

1   The first lady does not have a paying job. She is the wife of the president of the United States. But first ladies work hard. They greet important people. They help people learn to read or care for those who are sick.

2   Abigail Adams was one of the earliest and busiest first ladies. She often worked with her husband, John. In fact, many people thought she did too much. Sometimes she seemed to be running the country.

3   Another famous first lady was Eleanor Roosevelt. Her husband, Franklin, couldn't walk. So Mrs. Roosevelt traveled around the country for him. She talked to everyone. Then she went back to the White House. She told President Roosevelt what people were thinking and what they worried about. Mrs. Roosevelt also tried to make life better for America's poor people.

4   The people of the United States don't choose their first lady. She gets the job if her husband becomes president. Americans are lucky to have had so many hardworking women in the White House.

Circle the right answer for questions 1–5. Write your
answer to question 6 on a blank piece of paper.

1. The article does not tell _____.
   A who is first lady now
   B where the first lady lives
   C how a first lady gets the job
   D how much the first lady is paid

2. Which word in paragraph 1 means "welcome someone in a friendly way"?
   A work   C help
   B care   D greet

3. Which paragraph tells what Eleanor Roosevelt did?
   A 1   C 3
   B 2   D 4

4. The article does not say, but you can decide that first ladies _____.
   A keep the White House clean
   B spend all their time traveling
   C live apart from the rest of their family
   D do more than some people who have paying jobs

5. *Running* can have the following meanings. Mark the meaning used
   in paragraph 2.
   A entering a contest
   B making a short visit
   C leading or managing
   D going faster than a walk

6. If you were president or first lady of the United States, what would
   you do to help the country?

Is slime good to eat?

1   Everyone has seen the green slime in fish ponds and swimming pools. But not everyone knows that this slime is living and growing. It is an important plant called algae (AL•jee). Someday algae may be people's main food.

2   Algae are the tiniest of all plants. They have no stems, leaves, or roots. In fact, most algae are only one cell. But they are quite strong. They only need water, sunlight, and air to grow. And they grow very fast.

3   There are many different kinds of algae. They come in many colors like green, blue-green, red, and brown. Seaweed is one kind of algae that can be eaten. Astronauts in space eat this green food. Algae are easy to store on spaceships. And they are very good for people. But algae are more than a food. They also make oxygen. Someday people in space might need algae for both food and air.

4   A whole plate of algae is better for you than many whole dinners. But who wants to eat slimy green stuff? Most people don't. So cooks use algae in soups and salads. They even make an algae cheese cake! You can't tell you're eating slime.

Circle the right answer for questions 1–5. Write your answer to question 6 on a blank piece of paper.

1. The article does not tell how _____.
   A   algae are used in space
   B   fast algae grow
   C   small algae are
   D   algae taste

2. Which word in paragraph 2 means "the smallest part of a living plant"?
   A   air
   B   cell
   C   water
   D   sunlight

3. Which paragraph tells what cooks do with algae?
   A   1
   B   2
   C   3
   D   4

4. Which of these does not help algae grow?
   A   air
   B   stems
   C   water
   D   sunlight

5. The article does not say, but you can decide that many people don't know _____.
   A   that algae are alive
   B   that algae are slimy
   C   how good algae are for them to eat
   D   how algae look in ponds or swimming pools

6. Think of a food that tastes better than it looks. Tell about it.

How did the Liberty Bell become cracked?

1　The Liberty Bell is very old. It has been in Philadelphia, Pennsylvania, since 1752. For years, its ringing signaled important events. It cheered loudly when great leaders came to town. It cried softly when leaders died. The bell also brought people together. It called them to hear the Declaration of Independence on July 8, 1776.

2　The Liberty Bell is now silent. It has a very bad crack on one side. No one knows for sure how the crack started. It may have started when the bell was made. The bell cracked the first time it rang in 1752. But it was melted down and made again. Experts think a new crack started when the metal cooled. Each time the bell rang, the crack grew.

3　For a long time, the crack was too small to see. No one knew it was there at all. Then on July 8, 1835, the bell was ringing slowly. Suddenly, a large crack ripped across it. The bell was badly broken.

4　The Liberty Bell has been mostly quiet since then. But it still brings people together. Each year, thousands of people visit the famous bell.

Circle the right answer for questions 1–5. Write your answer to question 6 on a blank piece of paper.

1. The article does <u>not</u> tell _____.
   A   when the bell first cracked
   B   how old the bell is
   C   who rang the bell
   D   where the bell is

2. Which word in paragraph 2 means "people who know a lot about something"?
   A   bell
   B   crack
   C   metal
   D   experts

3. Which paragraph tells where the Liberty Bell is?
   A   1
   B   2
   C   3
   D   4

4. What happened last in the article?
   A   The Liberty Bell was rung for the first time.
   B   A large crack ripped across the Liberty Bell.
   C   People heard the Declaration of Independence.
   D   The Liberty Bell was melted down and made again.

5. The article does not say, but you can decide that long ago _____.
   A   bells were like TV or radio today
   B   important events happened in Philadelphia
   C   people didn't melt down metal and use it again
   D   bells were moved from other towns to Philadelphia

6. The Liberty Bell is an important symbol of the United States. Name another symbol of the country and tell how it is like and different from the Liberty Bell.

What are fossils?

1   What was life like millions of years ago? Fossils can give exciting clues! Fossils are the remains of ancient plants and animals. A fossil must be at least 10,000 years old.

2   There are many types of fossils. People have found the bones and fur of animals buried in ice. Other fossils are made of stone. In this case, plant or animal remains were pressed between layers of rock. Instead of decaying, the items turned to stone. Another type of fossil is the trace fossil. A trace fossil might show the shape of an animal's footprint or nest.

3   Most fossils are found in rock made from sand or mud. Over time, the rock wears away. Wind and water slowly break down the rock. Then a buried fossil may be exposed.

4   It can be fun to dig for fossils. In fact, the word *fossil* means "dug up." Cliffs are often good places to find fossils. Look for any object that seems different from the rocks around it. A three-year-old boy once found pieces of an ancient egg!

Circle the right answer for questions 1–5. Write your answer to question 6 on a blank piece of paper.

1. Fossils must be at least _____ years old.
   A 1,000
   B 10,000
   C 100,000
   D 1,000,000

2. Which word in paragraph 3 means "uncovered"?
   A wears
   B break
   C buried
   D exposed

3. Which paragraph tells how ancient remains were preserved as fossils?
   A 1
   B 2
   C 3
   D 4

4. Some remains of plants or animals turned to stone because they were _____.
   A covered by mud
   B buried under snow and ice
   C pressed between layers of rock
   D worn away by wind and water

5. The article does not say, but you can decide that trace fossils _____.
   A do not include rock
   B are older than other types of fossils
   C are more valuable than other fossils
   D do not contain plant or animal parts

6. What would you do if you found a fossil?

Who is Sandra Day O'Connor?

1   Sandra Day O'Connor was born in 1930. As a child, she lived with her parents at their cattle ranch in Arizona. When she grew up, she became a member of the Cowgirl Hall of Fame. She also became the first woman to serve on the U.S. Supreme Court.

2   Sandra was a strong student. She went to law school after college. Most students took three years to complete law school. But she earned her law degree in just two years. She also earned top grades.

3   Sandra was married in 1952. In the years that followed, she built her career and raised her three sons. No one would hire her as a lawyer at first. So, she started her own law office. Then she served as a state senator for five years. Later she worked as a judge for two state courts.

4   In 1981, Sandra Day O'Connor became the first female Justice of the U.S. Supreme Court. She served on the Court for 24 years. She played an important role in many of the Court's rulings. She set high standards for herself and others. "Do the best you can in every task," she said.

Correct pgs 11, 13 + 15

HOMEWORK

Circle the right answer for questions 1–5. Write your answer to question 6 on a blank piece of paper.

1. Sandra Day O'Connor served on the Supreme Court for _____ years.

   A 4

   B 14

   C 24

   D 30

2. Which word in paragraph 4 means "examples of good work"?

   A role

   B task

   C rulings

   D standards

3. The article tells mostly about the _____ of Sandra Day O'Connor.

   A career

   B schooling

   C family background

   D Supreme Court rulings

4. After serving as a state senator, Sandra Day O'Connor _____.

   A worked as a state court judge

   B earned her law degree

   C started a law office

   D got married

5. *Strong* can have the following meanings. Mark the meaning used in paragraph 2.

   A tough

   B sturdy

   C healthy

   D successful

6. Think about another famous American woman. Tell how this woman has inspired other women to follow their dreams.

What is a snow eater?

COLD AIR

1   A snow eater is a special wind. It blows only at certain places and times. One of these places is in the Rocky Mountains. The special time is most often late winter or early spring. The mountains are still covered with snow then.

2   One day a wind comes from the west. The wind blows up the west side of the mountain. It drops rain there. So it gets drier and drier as it climbs. Soon the wind reaches the top of the mountain. Cold air there keeps it from going higher.

3   Then the dry wind starts down the other side of the mountain. As it travels down, a strange thing happens. The wind becomes warmer and warmer. Its temperature can climb 30°F to 40°F in just a short time. The warm wind melts the snow at the foot of the mountain. As if by magic, animals can feed on grass that had been covered with snow only a few hours before.

4   This wind is called the snow eater or *chinook* (shuh•NOOK). The warm, dry wind may last only a few hours. Sometimes it lasts a few days. No one can tell when the snow eater will come again.

COLD AIR

Circle the right answer for questions 1–5. Write your answer to question 6 on a blank piece of paper.

1. The snow eater happens in the _____.
   A Rocky Mountains
   B White Mountains
   C Appalachian Mountains
   D Sierra Nevada Mountains

2. Which word in paragraph 3 means "how hot or cold something is"?
   A climb   C dry
   B temperature   D warm

3. Which paragraph tells another name for the snow eater?
   A 1   C 3
   B 2   D 4

4. The snow eater gets drier as it climbs because it _____.
   A gets cold
   B drops rain
   C melts snow
   D blows hard

5. *Foot* can have the following meanings. Mark the meaning used in paragraph 3.
   A motion of walking or running
   B part of a person's leg
   C the lowest part
   D 12 inches

6. Do you think *snow eater* is a good name for this wind? Tell why or why not.

Why did Native Americans make totem poles?

1   Many Native Americans used to think that animals watched over them. They called these animals totems (TOH•tumz). The word *totem* means "brother."

2   Old stories tell how each family got its own totem. In one Native American tale, an eagle brought fish to a hungry boy. The boy's family thought that the eagle was guarding him. They took the eagle as their totem. It became their special sign. When people saw a picture of an eagle, they knew which family it stood for.

3   Some Native Americans used to make hats or masks with their totems on them. Those near the Pacific Ocean did something else. These people were great wood carvers. They lived near tall forests. So they carved their totems into logs. The carvings are called totem poles. Each one told a story. These "story books" were then used in different ways. Some poles held up the roofs of houses. Others stood in front of homes to show who lived inside. Some totem poles even told about friends who had died.

4   Rain and time have destroyed many of these totem poles. But a few can still be found today. They tell a lot about the Native Americans who made them.

Circle the right answer for questions 1–5. Write your answer to question 6 on a blank piece of paper.

HOMEWORK

1. The article does <u>not</u> tell about _____.
   A where the wood carvers lived
   B old Native American tales
   C canoes carved from logs
   D what totem poles told

2. Which word in paragraph 3 means "tree trunks that have been cut"?
   A logs   C forests
   B poles   D carvers

3. Which paragraph tells why one family took an eagle for its totem?
   A 1   C 3
   B 2   D 4

4. Native Americans near the Pacific Ocean carved totems into logs mostly because they _____.
   A ran out of masks
   B liked carrying wood
   C lived near tall forests
   D needed to hold up their roofs

5. The article does not say, but you can decide that Native Americans _____ animals.
   A sold   C mocked
   B feared   D respected

6. Think about the animal you would want for your totem. Explain why you would choose this animal.

How are ladybugs useful?

1   The brightly colored ladybug has always been a farmer's friend. In the western United States, thousands of ladybugs fly to the fields each spring. After eating other insects, ladybugs lay their eggs and die.

2   In only five days, young ladybugs hatch and eat hungrily. They feed on insects called aphids (AY•fidz) that eat the farmers' plants. They eat most of the aphids in two or three weeks. Then the young ladybugs rest for a week. They change into the red-and-black bugs that people know.

3   The grown ladybugs are even hungrier than the young ladybugs were. But by now, there are very few aphids left to eat. The hungry ladybugs fly high into the air.

4   Warm winds carry them to the hills where they will find more food. The ladybugs stay there until the next spring.

5   The aphids come back as soon as the ladybugs leave. Again the aphids start eating plants. So some farmers buy sacks of ladybugs. Some of the ladybugs stay to eat the aphids. But others fly off to the hills. Farmers are looking for ways to keep the useful ladybug on the farm.

Circle the right answer for questions 1–5. Write your answer to question 6 on a blank piece of paper.

1. The article does <u>not</u> tell about the _____ of the ladybug.
   A   eggs
   B   food
   C   color
   (D) wings

HOMEWORK

2. Which word in paragraph 2 means "become different"?
   A   rest   C   hatch
   B   feed   (D) change

3. Which paragraph tells when ladybugs change colors?
   A   1   C   3
   (B) 2   D   4

4. What happens first after ladybugs are born?
   A   They change colors.
   (B) They feed on aphids.
   C   They rest for a week.
   D   They fly off to the hills.

5. The article does not say, but you can decide that ladybugs _____.
   A   live only in the East
   B   are afraid of people
   C   hurt farmers
   (D) have wings

6. What do you think farmers could do to keep ladybugs on their farms?

What is a barn raising?

1. The Amish (AH•mish) people of Pennsylvania still live as they did many years ago. They plow their fields with horses. They have no cars or electricity. They wear plain clothes.

2. The Amish believe in caring for their neighbors. When fire burns down a friend's barn, they all get together and build a new one. This is called a barn raising.

3. On the day of a barn raising, the Amish get up earlier than usual. First they do their own farm chores. Then whole families climb into their wagons. The horses take them to their neighbor's farm. More than 200 people may get there before 7 A.M.

4. Everyone pitches in to build the new barn. The men cut wood and hammer it into place. Some children carry nails and tools to workers. Others help their mothers cook delicious food. In the middle of the morning, everyone stops for a snack. At noon, they sit down to great dishes like chicken-corn soup and shoofly pie. By 4 P.M., the new barn is finished. Then the Amish go home. They helped a neighbor. And they had a chance to work, eat, and laugh together.

Circle the right answer for questions 1–5. Write your answer to question 6 on a blank piece of paper.

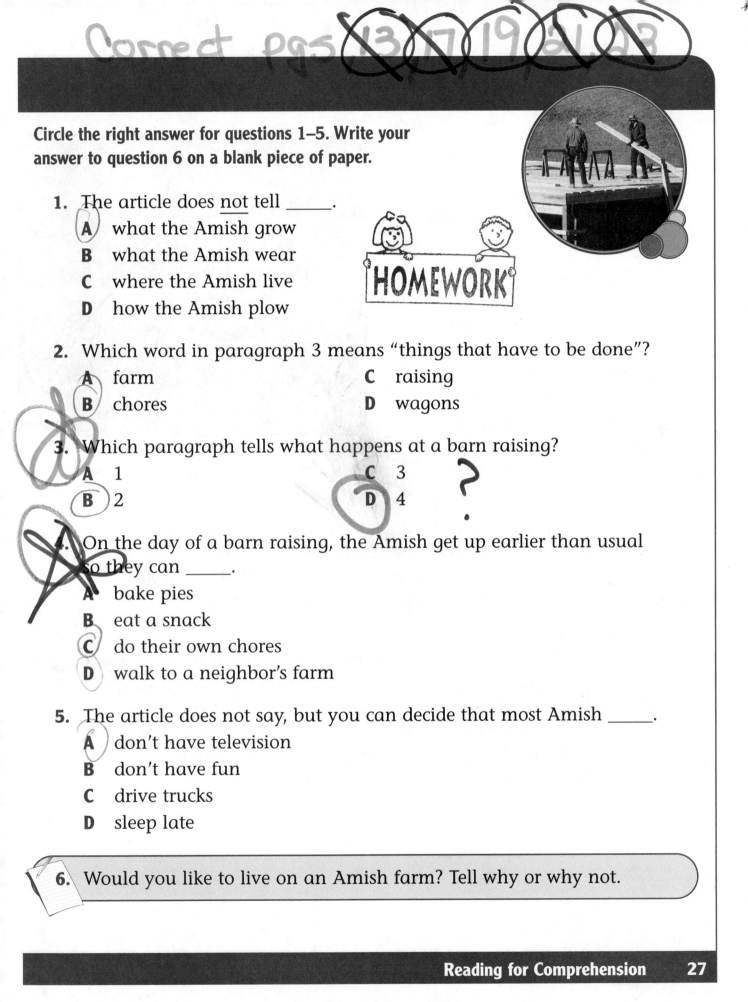

1. The article does <u>not</u> tell _____.
   A what the Amish grow
   B what the Amish wear
   C where the Amish live
   D how the Amish plow

HOMEWORK

2. Which word in paragraph 3 means "things that have to be done"?
   A farm
   B chores
   C raising
   D wagons

3. Which paragraph tells what happens at a barn raising?
   A 1
   B 2
   C 3
   D 4

4. On the day of a barn raising, the Amish get up earlier than usual so they can _____.
   A bake pies
   B eat a snack
   C do their own chores
   D walk to a neighbor's farm

5. The article does not say, but you can decide that most Amish _____.
   A don't have television
   B don't have fun
   C drive trucks
   D sleep late

6. Would you like to live on an Amish farm? Tell why or why not.

Does a giant redwood tree have giant roots?

1   Most trees have deep, wide roots. These roots feed the trees and hold them in the ground.

2   The redwood is the giant of trees. It can be as tall as a 25-story building. You might think that a redwood would have giant roots. But these huge trees grow on rocky ground. A redwood tree may have roots that are only eight feet deep.

3   Why doesn't the tree fall over? First, redwood roots really spread out. Just one redwood tree may have roots that cover a space the size of a football field. Redwood trees also grow very close together. The roots of one tree are tangled with the roots of many others. Each set of roots helps to hold all the trees in the ground.

4   What happens when many redwood trees are cut down all at once? The roots of other redwood trees around them are hurt. After a while, these trees die. The redwood forest thins out. There is more space between the trees. The wind can now blow down a tree. The redwood forest dies, tree by tree. It takes careful cutting and planting of new trees to keep redwood forests alive.

Reading for Comprehension

Circle the right answer for questions 1–5. Write your
answer to question 6 on a blank piece of paper.

1. Redwood trees _____.
   A   have deep roots
   B   have short trunks
   C   grow in sandy soil
   D   grow close together

2. Which word in paragraph 3 means "wrapped around each other"?
   A   together   C   spread
   B   tangled   D   cover

3. Which paragraph tells how a redwood forest can die?
   A   1   C   3
   B   2   D   4

4. The redwood forest thins out when _____.
   A   roots spread out
   B   roots tangle together
   C   trees grow on rocky ground
   D   trees are cut down all at once

5. The article does not say, but you can decide that redwood forests
   are _____.
   A   easy to cut down
   B   easy to walk through
   C   killed by careless people
   D   all over the United States

6. What do you think should be done about redwood forests? Should
   people keep cutting them down, cut less, or stop cutting? Tell why you
   think that.

What is it like to live on a houseboat?

1   Can you imagine living in a house that bobs up and down all the time? A place where you fall asleep each night to the sound of water lapping against the side? A house where you live and keep everything you own in just one small room? Well, that's what living on a houseboat is like.

2   Houseboats are real boats. People just choose to live on them. These people call themselves "liveaboards." Most houseboats are about 35 to 40 feet long and 12 feet wide. But inside are beds, closets, and a tiny kitchen and bathroom. Space can be very tight.

3   So why would anyone want to live on a boat? For one thing, it can be a lot of fun. Liveaboards can sail to different places whenever they want. They can stop to explore or decide to keep going. They can meet other liveaboards and share their adventures. They can also fish for dinner right off the side of their homes!

4   But living on a houseboat can be hard, too. During a storm, it can be very wobbly. And liveaboards have to be able to get along with each other. There's not much room to be alone on a houseboat.

Circle the right answer for questions 1–5. Write your answer to question 6 on a blank piece of paper.

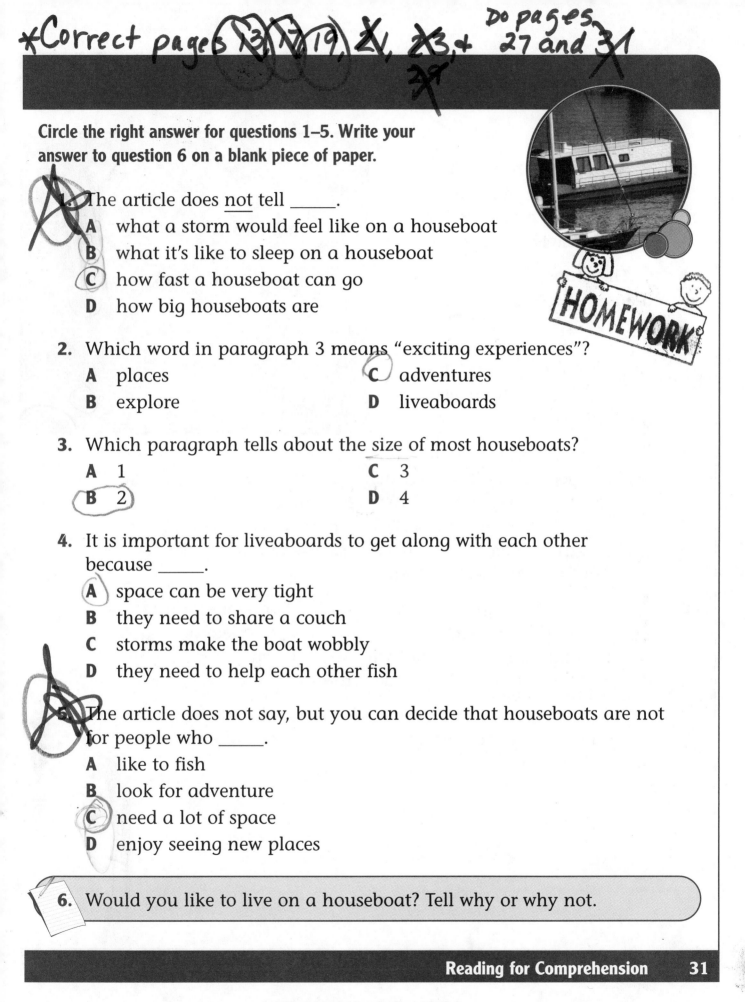

1. The article does <u>not</u> tell _____.
   A   what a storm would feel like on a houseboat
   B   what it's like to sleep on a houseboat
   C   how fast a houseboat can go
   D   how big houseboats are

2. Which word in paragraph 3 means "exciting experiences"?
   A   places   **C**   adventures
   B   explore   D   liveaboards

3. Which paragraph tells about the size of most houseboats?
   A   1   C   3
   B   2   D   4

4. It is important for liveaboards to get along with each other because _____.
   A   space can be very tight
   B   they need to share a couch
   C   storms make the boat wobbly
   D   they need to help each other fish

5. The article does not say, but you can decide that houseboats are not for people who _____.
   A   like to fish
   B   look for adventure
   C   need a lot of space
   D   enjoy seeing new places

6. Would you like to live on a houseboat? Tell why or why not.

How does a dragonfly use its legs?

1   A dragonfly has six long legs. They are not made for walking. The dragonfly has another use for its legs.

2   The dragonfly is one of the fastest flying insects in the world. It goes 50 to 60 miles an hour. Its four large wings are always open. It is easy for it to catch up with other insects.

3   As the dragonfly flies, it bends its legs under its body. Each leg is covered with stiff hairs, or spines. These legs and their spines form a kind of basket. The dragonfly flies above an insect. As it passes over, it catches the insect in the basket formed by its legs. The dragonfly picks the insect out of the basket and eats it.

4   The dragonfly mostly eats while it flies. Sometimes it may stop to eat a large insect. Then its legs cling to a leaf or twig. It can even take a few steps. But with such strong wings, a dragonfly doesn't need legs to get around.

5   A dragonfly spends every daylight minute looking for food. It seems to know it doesn't have much time. The dragonfly lives only a few weeks.

Circle the right answer for questions 1–5. Write your answer to question 6 on a blank piece of paper.

1. The article does <u>not</u> tell about the _____ of the dragonfly.
   A   legs
   B   color
   C   wings
   D   speed

2. Which word in paragraph 4 means "hold on tightly"?
   A   stop   C   cling
   B   take   D   strong

3. Which paragraph tells how many wings the dragonfly has?
   A   1   C   3
   B   2   D   4

4. Before the dragonfly can catch an insect in its basket, it must _____.
   A   take a few steps
   B   fly above the insect
   C   fly beside the insect
   D   cling to a leaf or twig

5. The article does not say, but you can decide that dragonflies _____.
   A   don't eat at night
   B   don't use their legs
   C   never eat small insects
   D   like to eat standing still

6. What would it be like if you could fly? Tell about what you would do.

What is a love apple?

1   Indians in South America once grew many plants that no one else had seen. One of these plants had green leaves with bright fruit. The Indians called it the *tomatl* (toh•MAH•tuhl). In the 1500s, Spaniards came to the New World. They saw the strange new plant and gathered its seeds to send to Spain.

2   The plant was pretty. People in Spain began to grow the *tomate,* as they called it, in their flower gardens. Soon it was being grown in other countries, too. Each time the plant found a new home, it also found a new name. In Italy, the fruit was called the "apple of gold." In France, it became known as the "apple of love." For the next 300 years, people called tomatoes "love apples."

3   People grew love apples with their roses. They put the pretty plants in vases and set them on their tables. But no one ate the fruit. People thought that love apples were dangerous to eat. In fact, love apples were sometimes tossed to wolves to kill them. This gave love apples still another name—"wolf peaches."

4   Very slowly, people learned that love apples were safe to eat. Today, tomatoes are a favorite food of people all over the world.

Circle the right answer for questions 1–5. Write your
answer to question 6 on a blank piece of paper.

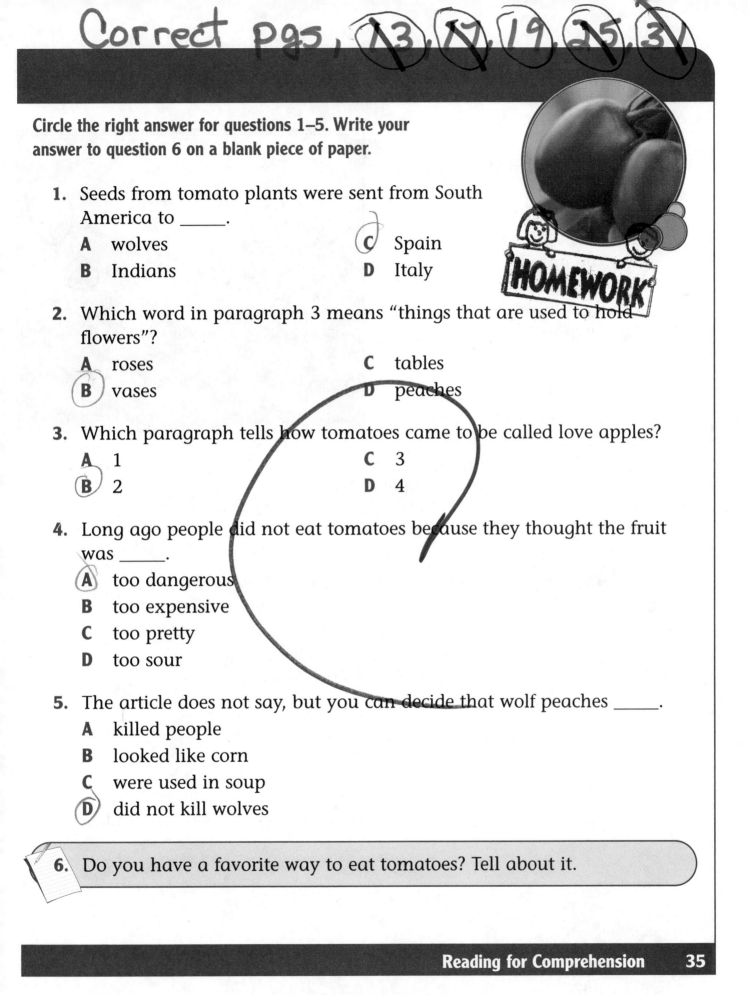

1. Seeds from tomato plants were sent from South
   America to _____.
   A wolves   C Spain
   B Indians   D Italy

2. Which word in paragraph 3 means "things that are used to hold
   flowers"?
   A roses   C tables
   B vases   D peaches

3. Which paragraph tells how tomatoes came to be called love apples?
   A 1   C 3
   B 2   D 4

4. Long ago people did not eat tomatoes because they thought the fruit
   was _____.
   A too dangerous
   B too expensive
   C too pretty
   D too sour

5. The article does not say, but you can decide that wolf peaches _____.
   A killed people
   B looked like corn
   C were used in soup
   D did not kill wolves

6. Do you have a favorite way to eat tomatoes? Tell about it.

Reading for Comprehension   35

Does it ever snow in the desert?

1   A place is called a desert because it is very dry. Many people think that deserts must be hot as well as dry. They are only half right. It is true that the world's deserts are always dry. It is not true that all of them are always hot.

2   In hot parts of the world, the deserts are hot all year round. But even these hot deserts cool down at night.

3   In cooler parts of the world, the deserts are cold at night. They are also cold in winter. Many frozen places in the world are also deserts. The ice cap of Greenland, for example, is an ice desert.

4   All deserts, hot or cold, get some rain. It may last only a few minutes. And it may come only once a year. But sometimes this rain falls on a cold desert in winter. When that happens, cold air changes the rain to snow. In fact, cold deserts high in the mountains often get snowstorms. So the answer is yes, it does snow in the desert.

Circle the right answer for questions 1–5. Write your answer to question 6 on a blank piece of paper.

1. The article does <u>not</u> tell about _____ in the desert.
   A rain
   B snow
   C plants
   D winter

2. Which word in paragraph 3 means "turned into ice"?
   A cooler   C winter
   B frozen   D night

3. Which paragraph tells about the ice cap in Greenland?
   A 1   C 3
   B 2   D 4

4. The article does not say, but you can decide that cold deserts _____.
   A do not get many days of snow
   B are always on flat land
   C are only cold at night
   D get heavy rain

5. *Cap* can have the following meanings. Mark the meaning used in paragraph 3.
   A fitting for the end of a tube
   B natural cover or top
   C limit
   D hat

6. Which would you rather visit, a hot desert or a cold one? Why?

Who was Laika?

1   People first heard about Laika in 1957. That year on November 3, the Soviet Union sent a satellite (SA•tuh•lyt) into space. It was called Sputnik 2. The world's first space traveler was onboard. She was a dog named Laika, which means "barker."

2   Until Sputnik 2 went up, no one knew what would happen to living things in space. Could animals live there? Could people travel safely in spaceships? What dangers would there be in space? Laika's trip answered many of these questions.

3   For seven days the dog circled Earth. She lived in a special cabin that was kept cool for her. Laika barked and moved about. She got food the same way she had been trained to get it on Earth. The dog was well and happy. She showed people that animals could live in space. Maybe men and women could, too.

4   The Russians didn't know how to bring Laika back to Earth. She died in space. Since then, people have learned a lot about safe space travel. But they haven't forgotten Laika. Her spaceship will always be known as Muttnik 2.

Correct 13, 17, 19, 25, 27, 29, 31, 33

Circle the right answer for questions 1–5. Write your answer to question 6 on a blank piece of paper.

1. From Laika's trip, people learned that _____.
   A dogs are smarter than horses
   B animals could live in space
   C dogs don't bark in space
   D dogs like to travel

2. Which word in paragraph 3 means "taught"?
   A live
   B showed
   C trained
   D circled

3. Which paragraph tells when Sputnik 2 went into space?
   A 1
   B 2
   C 3
   D 4

4. Laika died in space because the Russians _____.
   A didn't train the dog to eat
   B didn't make the cabin cool
   C didn't allow the dog to move around
   D didn't know how to bring the satellite back

5. The article does not say, but you can decide that _____.
   A the Russians never sent another satellite into space
   B the Russians had a way to watch Laika in space
   C scientists didn't learn much from Laika's trip
   D another animal has never gone into space

6. Laika was the world's first space traveler. What would you like to be first to do? Why?

What are Saturn's rings?

1   In 1610, a scientist named Galileo looked through his telescope and saw Saturn. It looked to him like a large planet with two small moons next to it. Later, better telescopes showed that Saturn had rings around it. Now people know much more about Saturn's rings. But there is still much to learn.

2   Saturn is a huge planet. It is made mostly of gas. So it has no solid surface. The rings are not solid either. They are made of pieces of ice, dust, and rock. Some pieces are small as grains of sand. Others are as large as skyscrapers.

3   Saturn's rings are very wide and half a mile thick. They include many separate rings. A space divides the rings into two main parts. This gap is called the Cassini Division. A smaller division is called the Encke Gap. One of Saturn's moons orbits near this area.

4   No one knows for sure how the rings were made. They may be material left over from when the planet was formed. Or an asteroid may have smashed one of Saturn's moons. Someday people may learn the truth. But until then, Saturn's rings are still a mystery.

Circle the right answer for questions 1–5. Write your
answer to question 6 on a blank piece of paper.

1. The planet Saturn is mostly made of _____.
   A ice
   B gas
   C dust
   D rock

2. Which word in paragraph 3 means "an open space"?
   A gap   C wide
   B area   D parts

3. Which paragraph tells about the shape of Saturn's rings?
   A 1   C 3
   B 2   D 4

4. People see two main areas of rings around Saturn because of _____.
   A the Cassini Division
   B Saturn's moons
   C the Encke Gap
   D ice particles

5. The article does not say, but you can decide that scientists _____.
   A will eventually visit Saturn
   B think Saturn is a small planet
   C still have a lot to learn about Saturn
   D haven't seen any moons near Saturn

6. Tell about something you enjoyed seeing in the night sky, with or
   without a telescope. What made this so interesting?

1   Do you know a person who served in the armed forces? Maybe your grandfather was in the army. Maybe a family friend was in the navy. Maybe your neighbor was a marine. Maybe your aunt was in the air force.

2   People who served in the armed forces are called veterans. They served the United States in times of war or peace. There are almost 25 million veterans living in this country. November 11 is a special day for them.

3   The First World War ended on November 11, 1918. This day became a holiday. It was a time to thank soldiers who fought in the war. In 1954 the holiday changed. It was named Veterans Day. It became a special day for all men and women who were in the armed forces. They risked their lives to keep Americans safe and free. On this day, some towns have parades, and many people display flags. Schools and post offices are closed.

4   There is another special day for veterans in May. It is called Memorial Day. On this day, Americans honor military men and women who lost their lives when they served our country.

Circle the right answer for questions 1–5. Write your answer to question 6 on a blank piece of paper.

1. November 11, 1918 was the date that _____.
   A the Second World War ended
   B the First World War ended
   C Veterans Day was named
   D Memorial Day began

2. Which word in paragraph 4 means "to show respect for"?
   A special
   B military
   C lives
   D honor

3. Which paragraph tells the number of veterans living in the United States?
   A 1
   B 2
   C 3
   D 4

4. In 1954 the holiday changed in order to thank _____.
   A the families of veterans
   B veterans of the First World War
   C veterans who died
   D all veterans

5. The article does not say, but you can decide that Veterans Day is the time to honor _____.
   A veterans who are still living
   B veterans who died
   C America's leaders
   D new soldiers

6. What is one thing you could do to thank American veterans on Veterans Day? Tell why this would be a good thing to do.

What are lantern fish?

1 Lantern fish are fish that carry their own lights. You must dive deep into the ocean to find them. As you go deeper and deeper, the daylight grows dimmer and dimmer. At 500 feet below the surface, the daylight is almost gone. The water is dark blue. That's where you will find lantern fish.

2 There are over 230 different kinds of lantern fish. Most are only about as long as your fingers. Even the biggest are no more than six inches long. Yet each lantern fish has as many as 100 small round lights underneath its body. Each kind of lantern fish has its lights placed in a different way. The fish use their lights to signal one another and to help them catch food.

3 Most lantern fish are brown on top and silver underneath. They have very large eyes. Lantern fish eat smaller sea animals like shrimp and sea butterflies. At night they may swim up near the surface of the ocean. Their lights shine like stars under the water. Lantern fish are one of the wonders of the sea.

Circle the right answer for questions 1–5. Write your answer to question 6 on a blank piece of paper.

1. The article does not tell about the _____ of a lantern fish.

   A   size   C   food
   B   eggs   D   color

2. Which word in paragraph 1 means "the outer or top part of an object or body"?

   A   dive   C   surface
   B   water   D   daylight

3. The lantern fish uses its lights to catch food and _____.

   A   swim faster   C   signal fishermen
   B   attract food   D   signal other lantern fish

4. The article does not say, but you can decide that lantern fish _____.

   A   don't like water with a lot of daylight
   B   don't need their lights to survive
   C   eat fish 12 inches and longer
   D   travel alone

5. *Placed* can have the following meanings. Mark the meaning used in paragraph 2.

   A   positioned
   B   directed to a spot
   C   assigned to a job
   D   remembered somebody

6. From above, lantern fish look like dark brown seaweed. From below, they look like daylight shining through the water. How do you think this helps them?

How did stories about mermaids start?

1   A mermaid is a beautiful woman with the tail of a fish. Long ago, lonely men at sea told stories about seeing mermaids. But what they probably saw was a sea cow, or manatee.

2   A manatee might look like a mermaid from far away. It has short front legs shaped like paddles. They might be mistaken for arms. A mother manatee holds her baby in these "arms."

3   You certainly wouldn't mistake a manatee for a mermaid after a closer look. It's hard to call this sea animal beautiful. It has a square face and gray skin. Short hairs stick out here and there. The manatee's huge body ends in a rounded tail. It can be more than 13 feet long and weigh up to 3,500 pounds.

4   Some old stories say that mermaids are harmful. But manatees hurt no animal or person. They just eat plants. When they eat, you can hear the noise 200 yards away. Because manatees are both friendly and slow, they are easy to catch. Some are killed for their meat, oil, and skin. Others are run over by boats. If manatees aren't better protected, they may soon be found only in stories, just like mermaids.

Circle the right answer for questions 1–5. Write your answer to question 6 on a blank piece of paper.

HOMEWORK

1. The article does <u>not</u> tell about the _____ of a manatee.

   A skin   **C** tail

   B eyes   **D** size

2. Which word in paragraph 4 means "kept safe"?

   A killed   **C** protected

   B found   **D** harmful

3. Which paragraph tells what a mermaid is?

   A 1   **C** 3

   B 2   **D** 4

4. A manatee might look like a mermaid from far away mostly because of its _____.

   A gray skin

   B square face

   C rounded tail

   D short front legs

5. The article does not say, but you can decide that manatees _____.

   A swim near the surface of the water

   B resemble a beautiful woman

   C can easily avoid hunters

   D have attacked surfers

6. A manatee is also called "sea cow." Explain why you think the manatee has that name.

How does an earthworm dig tunnels?

1   An earthworm has no feet or claws. Its body is small and soft. How does an earthworm dig tunnels?

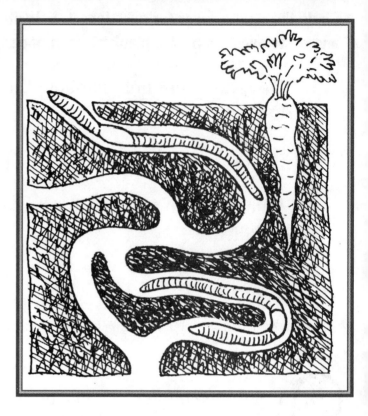

2   Every earthworm has tiny hairs on the bottom of its body. These hairs help the worm move along the ground. If the soil is loose, the earthworm just pushes it to one side to make a tunnel.

3   Most of the time, though, the earthworm makes its tunnels by eating. It uses its mouth to take bits of soil into its body. There are tiny pieces of plant leaves and stems in the soil. The earthworm uses them for food. It pushes the rest of the soil out of its body in wiggly shapes called castings. Worm castings make good food for growing plants.

4   Earthworms dig winding tunnels 12 to 18 inches deep in the earth. Each tiny tunnel lets rain and air reach the roots of growing plants. Without these tunnels, the ground would be dry and hard. The earthworm may not be much to look at. But this tiny earth-moving "machine" is one of a farmer's best friends.

Circle the right answer for questions 1–5. Write your answer to question 6 on a blank piece of paper.

1. The article does <u>not</u> tell about the _____ of an earthworm.

   A food　　　　　　　　　**C** body

   B color　　　　　　　　　**D** tunnels

2. Which word in paragraph 3 means "parts of plants that hold up the leaves"?

   A stems　　　　　　　　　**C** pieces

   B shapes　　　　　　　　　**D** tunnels

3. Which paragraph tells how earthworms move along the ground?

   A 1　　　　　　　　　　　**C** 3

   B 2　　　　　　　　　　　**D** 4

4. Earthworms are helpful to farmers because _____.

   A they trim plants

   B they eat garbage

   C their tunnels help plants grow

   D their tunnels make the garden prettier

5. *Reach* can have the following meanings. Mark the meaning used in paragraph 4.

   A talk with

   B stretch out

   C hand over

   D extend to

6. Earthworms breathe through their skin. They get air from between bits of soil. Why do you think they come up to the top of the soil when it rains?

What are the Mayan pyramids?

1   What picture does the word *pyramid* bring to mind? You probably think of ancient Egypt. But did you know that New World people built pyramids, too? The ancient Maya lived in what is now Central America. They built many great pyramids between A.D. 250 and 900.

2   Mayan pyramids are different from those in Egypt. Egyptian pyramids were tombs. Kings, queens, and other important people were buried in them. Some Mayan pyramids were tombs, too. But most were used for religious ceremonies. Priests would ask the gods for help in battle or with crops.

3   Mayan pyramids are between 100 and 200 feet high. They are not as tall as Egyptian pyramids. Steps go up the side. The Maya used them to climb up to the flat top. On the top of most Mayan pyramids is a small building. This is where the Maya held their religious ceremonies.

4   But Mayan pyramids are like Egyptian pyramids in some ways. They are made of huge blocks of stone. It took thousands of people many years to build each one. And both kinds of pyramids help people today learn about ancient people.

Circle the right answer for questions 1–5. Write your answer to question 6 on a blank piece of paper.

1. Mayan pyramids are not as _____ as Egyptian pyramids.
   - A   beautiful
   - B   well built
   - C   tall
   - D   new

2. Which word in paragraph 2 means "important acts done at special times"?
   - A   kings
   - B   tombs
   - C   pyramids
   - D   ceremonies

3. Which paragraph tells how Mayan pyramids are like Egyptian pyramids?
   - A   1
   - B   2
   - C   3
   - D   4

4. The article does not say, but you can decide that the Maya held religious gatherings on top of pyramids because _____.
   - A   there was more sunlight there
   - B   they wanted to be closer to the gods
   - C   that was the only place that was flat
   - D   they built the top of the pyramid before they built other parts

5. *Picture* can have the following meanings. Mark the meaning used in paragraph 1.
   - A   design made by painting
   - B   mental image
   - C   situation
   - D   movie

6. Think of the oldest building in your town. How is it used? How is it like and different from the Mayan pyramids?

What are feral animals?

1   Have you ever heard of feral (FIR•uhl) animals? Maybe you haven't. But you probably have seen some. Most feral animals are wild animals that used to be tame. Some of these animals were born feral.

2   Most feral animals are dogs or cats. Many were pets. But the owners got tired of them or moved. So they let the animals go. These owners just let their dogs and cats loose in the country or city.

3   What happens to these animals? The lucky ones find new owners to care for them. But most do not. They become wild. They eat garbage to stay alive. And they kill small wild animals or farm animals for food. Feral animals don't live very long. Most live less than two years. They get hungry or sick. Dogcatchers catch them, too. And some farmers poison them for killing their animals.

4   There are millions of feral animals. They are a danger to real wild animals. But there wouldn't be any feral animals if people found good homes for pets they no longer want. Then the animals would not have to turn wild to stay alive.

Circle the right answer for questions 1–5. Write your answer to question 6 on a blank piece of paper.

1. The article does <u>not</u> tell how feral animals _____.
   A learn to kill for food
   B become wild
   C sleep
   D die

2. Which word in paragraph 4 means "something that can cause harm"?
   A danger   C alive
   B longer   D wild

3. Which paragraph tells how many feral animals there are?
   A 1   C 3
   B 2   D 4

4. Feral animals become wild mostly because _____.
   A they ran away from home
   B their owners let them go
   C they lived on a farm
   D they got sick

5. The article does not say, but you can decide that feral animals _____.
   A live a long time
   B find new homes fast
   C have a very hard life
   D are friendly to other animals

6. Feral animals are a problem in many places—in cities, the suburbs, and the country. Write a letter to your city government. Give them two ideas of things they can do to help with the problem.

What are the blues?

1   The blues are a special kind of music. Blues songs can be slow or fast. Most are sad. They tell about hard times and people's troubles.

2   For a long time, blues songs were mostly listened to and enjoyed by African Americans in the South. The rest of the country hardly knew about them. Then William Christopher Handy came along. He made the blues famous, not just in the United States but all over the world.

3   W. C. Handy was born in Alabama in 1873. As a young boy, he taught himself to play the cornet. But music was not allowed in the Handy home. So W. C. went away. He had no money. He had to travel in the boxcar of a train because he couldn't buy a ticket. When he got to St. Louis, Missouri, he was tired and hungry. He wrote a song about his troubles. That song is called "The St. Louis Blues." It became known everywhere.

4   Soon everyone was singing the blues. People loved songs like "Blues in the Night" and "Basin Street Blues." W. C. Handy gave Americans some great music.

Circle the right answer for questions 1–5. Write your
answer to question 6 on a blank piece of paper.

1. The article does <u>not</u> tell about _____.
   - A titles of other blues songs
   - B "The St. Louis Blues"
   - C W. C. Handy
   - D rock and roll

2. Which word in paragraph 3 means "a kind of horn"?
   - A boxcar
   - B cornet
   - C ticket
   - D song

3. Which paragraph tells who mostly liked the blues at first?
   - A 1
   - B 2
   - C 3
   - D 4

4. W. C. Handy traveled in the boxcar of a train because _____.
   - A he was afraid of planes
   - B he could play music there
   - C he had no money for a ticket
   - D that was the only way to get to St. Louis

5. *Rest* can have the following meanings. Mark the meaning used
   in paragraph 2.
   - A other parts
   - B take it easy
   - C a stop in music
   - D remain confident

6. What music do you most like to listen to? Tell what you like about it.

How can scents change the way you feel?

1   Has the smell of something ever made you think of a spring day? Do some scents make you happy? Do others relax you?

2   Believe it or not, scents can change the way a person feels. Each day scientists learn more about this. They have people sniff different odors. Then they ask what each smell reminds them of or how it makes them feel. Now scientists are trying different scents to make people feel better.

3   Scientists now understand what certain odors do. One thing they know is that lemons remind people of things that are fresh and clean. So people who make cleaners and soaps for the home often put lemon scent in them.

4   The smell of vanilla helps people relax. Its scent may be piped into the air in hospitals. A peppermint scent keeps people awake. This may be used in office buildings. People need to be sharp when they're working. Cinnamon and apple smells remind many people of their homes. Some stores put these scents in the air to make people comfortable. That way they'll want to buy something.

5   And why shouldn't smells make you feel good? When it comes to scents, the nose knows!

Circle the right answer for questions 1–5. Write your
answer to question 6 on a blank piece of paper.

1. The article does not tell what scent makes you
   feel _____.
   A fresh
   B awake
   C hungry
   D comfortable

2. Which word in paragraph 4 means "cozy and easy"?
   A comfortable
   B scent
   C awake
   D sharp

3. Which paragraph tells how scientists learn about odors?
   A 1
   B 2
   C 3
   D 4

4. The smell of peppermint helps people stay _____.
   A home
   B clean
   C awake
   D relaxed

5. The article does not say, but you can decide that cinnamon and apple
   remind people of their homes because _____.
   A cooking goes on there
   B cleaning goes on there
   C they smell like a hospital
   D all homes smell like cinnamon

6. What is your favorite smell? What does it remind you of? How does it
   make you feel?

1   Mary Eliza Mahoney was born in 1845. She always wanted to be a nurse. It was hard for her to find a nursing school, though. Nurses' training had just gotten started. And there were no African American nurses. Finally, a Boston school let Mary Eliza in.

2   Mary Eliza worked hard in nursing school. She was one of the best in her class. She wanted to be a good nurse. Mary Eliza also wanted to set an example. Then other African Americans would be able to train as nurses. Her idea worked. Soon five more black women got into nursing school.

3   In 1879, Mary Eliza finished school. It should have been easy for her to get a job in a hospital. But it wasn't. In those days, hospitals wouldn't hire African American nurses. Instead, Mary Eliza worked as a nurse in people's homes. She also helped start a special group. They fought for jobs and fair pay for black nurses. Today, thousands of African Americans are hospital nurses. In a way, they have their jobs because of Mary Eliza Mahoney.

Circle the right answer for questions 1–5. Write your answer to question 6 on a blank piece of paper.

1. The article does <u>not</u> tell about _____.
    A Mary Eliza's career
    B African American women
    C doctors
    D nursing school

2. Which word in paragraph 3 means "work to do"?
    A job
    B nurse
    C school
    D hospital

3. What happened last in the life of Mary Eliza Mahoney?
    A She finished nursing school.
    B Black nurses were hired in hospitals.
    C She worked as a nurse in people's homes.
    D Five other black women got into nursing school.

4. Mary Eliza worked as a nurse in people's homes because _____.
    A the pay was better
    B she did not finish school
    C hospitals would not hire her
    D there were no hospitals near her

5. *Train* can have the following meanings. Mark the meaning used in paragraph 2.
    A become something by studying and practicing
    B group of railroad cars pulled by an engine
    C direct the growth of something
    D make prepared for a test

6. Write a list of words that you think tell what kind of person Mary Eliza Mahoney was.

Why do groundhogs dig up fields?

1   Early settlers in America grew angry with a small, fat animal. It looked like a squirrel with a short tail. The animal dug up their fields and hurt their plants. Native Americans had named this animal "the digger." The settlers called it the groundhog.

2   The groundhog digs up fields to make a home for its winter sleep. It chooses a sandy place where the rainwater dries up quickly. Then it digs a tunnel with several rooms. These rooms are higher than the tunnel. Even if water runs into the tunnel, the rooms stay dry.

3   Groundhog holes always have two entrances. Some have more. The front entrance is wide and ringed with earth. A groundhog can jump in quickly if it has to. The back "door" is hidden in grass. It may be as far as 30 feet from the front entrance.

4   Other animals like the plan of the groundhog home. One man watched a groundhog's home over the winter. He found that the hole was also used by a rabbit, a skunk, a raccoon, and a family of foxes.

Circle the right answer for questions 1–5. Write your answer to question 6 on a blank piece of paper.

1. The article does <u>not</u> tell about the _____ of a groundhog.
   - **A** tail
   - **B** color
   - **C** home
   - **D** digging

2. Which word in paragraph 3 means "way to get in"?
   - **A** holes
   - **B** front
   - **C** back
   - **D** entrance

3. Which paragraph tells which other animals may use the groundhog's home?
   - **A** 1
   - **B** 2
   - **C** 3
   - **D** 4

4. The groundhog digs rooms higher than the tunnel so it can _____.
   - **A** stay dry
   - **B** trap foxes
   - **C** jump in quickly
   - **D** hide from foxes

5. The article does not say, but you can decide that a groundhog makes two entrances _____.
   - **A** to let in air
   - **B** to let in water
   - **C** so other animals can get in
   - **D** so it won't get trapped inside

6. Farmers have tried many things to keep groundhogs from digging up their fields. Nothing seems to work. What do you think might work?

1   Some women in Japan have unusual jobs. They are pearl divers. They dive to the bottom of the sea for oysters. The pearls are inside the oysters' shells. These women are called *ama.* This means "women of the sea" in Japanese. Their mothers and grandmothers were divers before them. Some ama dive in shallow water. They are *kachido.* That means "walking people." Others go out to sea in boats. They dive in deeper water. These women are *funado.* That means "ship people."

2   Ama use just a few tools when they dive. They carry knives to cut the oysters from the rocks. Ama wear goggles over their eyes. They tie stones around themselves to make their bodies heavy. And they have a rope lifeline tied around them. But the ama do not have tanks of air. These women hold their breath under the water. Each time they dive, they stay down for a full minute. Then they tug on their lifelines, and someone pulls them up. Ama may dive 100 times each day.

3   The ama have been diving for about 2,000 years. But now city jobs look better than diving jobs to many young girls. They may not follow their mothers into the sea. This ancient job might come to an end.

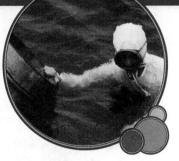

Circle the right answer for questions 1–5. Write your answer to question 6 on a blank piece of paper.

1. The funado dive _____.
   A in deeper water
   B in shallow water
   C 2,000 times a day
   D for buried treasure

2. Which word in paragraph 2 means "pull hard"?
   A carry   C cut
   B dive   D tug

3. To help them sink to the bottom of the sea, ama _____.
   A tie stones around themselves
   B take deep breaths
   C pull on a rope
   D wear goggles

4. The article does not say, but you can decide that _____.
   A ama don't allow men to help them
   B ama can't swim well
   C most ama are heavy
   D ama have a hard job

5. *Over* can have the following meanings. Mark the meaning used in paragraph 2.
   A ended   C on top of
   B larger than   D above

6. What do you think you'd have to do to train to be an ama?

Does music charm snakes?

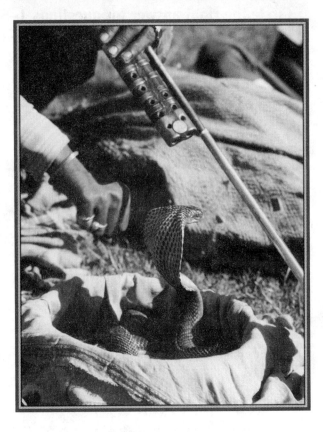

1.   The snake charmer from India plays his flute. A cobra rises slowly from its basket. People stand back from the poisonous snake. The snake charmer keeps playing. His body moves back and forth. The snake moves with him. It seems to dance to the music. Does the music have the power to tame this dangerous animal?

2.   This is all an act. And it's not as dangerous as it looks. For one thing, the snake's poison has been removed. The snake can't hear, either. So it isn't really dancing. The music is just to please the people watching the trick.

3.   The snake would just as soon nap in its basket. With the flute, the charmer blows air onto the snake's back. This makes the animal rise. The snake thinks the flute might be an enemy. So it watches the flute and moves with it. But the charmer must keep the snake moving. He can't let it lose interest. If it does, it will sink back into its basket. Also, the charmer must not frighten the snake or it will try to get away.

4.   The snake charmer's power over the snake doesn't come from his music. It comes from what he knows about snakes.

Circle the right answer for questions 1–5. Write your
answer to question 6 on a blank piece of paper.

1. The snake moves back and forth because it _____.
   A gets scared
   B seeks the light
   C likes the music
   D follows the flute

2. Which word in paragraph 1 means "not wild"?
   A flute   C tame
   B forth   D power

3. Which paragraph tells why the snake isn't dangerous?
   A 1   C 3
   B 2   D 4

4. The snake will sink back into its basket if it _____.
   A gets hungry
   B loses interest
   C sees the flute
   D gets frightened

5. *Sink* can have the following meanings. Mark the meaning used
   in paragraph 3.
   A something to hold in water
   B slope gradually
   C grow weaker
   D fall slowly

6. Which wild animal would you choose to have power over? Why?

What was the riddle of the sphinx?

1   The sphinx (SFINKS) was a make-believe animal of long ago. It had the head of a person, the body of a lion, and the wings of a bird. The sphinx lived near the city of Thebes (THEEBZ). When people entered Thebes, they had to pass by the sphinx. But the animal killed them unless they gave the right answer to a riddle.

2   The sphinx asked this question: "What has four legs in the morning, two legs at noon, and three legs at night?" No one could think of the answer.

3   At last, a man came to Thebes and solved the riddle. "I know what has four legs, then two, and then three," he said. "A person does. The time of day is like the times of a person's life. Morning is the beginning of the day. In the morning of life, people are babies. They crawl on all fours. Noon is the middle of the day. In the middle of life, people walk on two legs. Night is the end of the day. At the end of life, people are old. They use canes. That gives them three legs."

4   The sphinx was so angry that it jumped off the mountain and died. The people of Thebes were happy that the sphinx was gone. They made this wise man their king.

Circle the right answer for questions 1–5. Write your answer to question 6 on a blank piece of paper.

1. The article does <u>not</u> tell _____.
   A the wise man's name
   B what the sphinx did
   C the name of the city
   D what the riddle was

2. Which word in paragraph 3 means "figured out"?
   A said   **C** gives
   B came   **D** solved

3. Which paragraph tells the answer to the riddle?
   A 1   **C** 3
   B 2   **D** 4

4. The article does not say, but you can decide that the sphinx _____.
   A was friendly
   B could not speak
   C was king of Thebes
   D killed many people

5. *Right* can have the following meanings. Mark the meaning used in paragraph 1.
   A promise given by a law
   B opposite of left
   C straight
   D correct

6. Write your own riddle. See if a friend can answer it.

What are ant colonies?

1   Ants are very social insects. They live under the ground in nests called colonies. Some colonies have just a few ants. Other colonies have many more. A colony can have more than 100 million ants! Each colony is highly organized.

2   Each ant in a colony has a clear role. The queen ant's main role is to lay eggs. Other female ants are the workers. They find food, build the nest, care for baby ants, and feed the queen. The role of male ants is to mate with the queen.

3   The ants' colony has a number of chambers under the ground. Tunnels connect the chambers and lead to the exit. Some chambers are for storing food. Other chambers hold the baby ants. To make new tunnels, the worker ants carry tiny pieces of dirt to the surface. This forms an anthill.

4   The ants work together for the good of the colony. They use chemicals called pheromones (FAIR•o•mones) to give each other messages. For example, an ant will leave a trail of pheromones to lead other ants to a food source. Some ants even make chains by holding onto each other. The ants use these chains as bridges.

Circle the right answer for questions 1–5. Write your answer to question 6 on a blank piece of paper.

1. The main role of the queen ant is to _____.
   A lay eggs
   B make tunnels
   C care for baby ants
   D give directions to workers

2. Which word in paragraph 1 means "living in a group"?
   A organized   C under
   B social   D nests

3. Which paragraph tells about the jobs that different ants perform?
   A 1   C 3
   B 2   D 4

4. An ant will leave a trail of pheromones in order to _____.
   A make a chain
   B hold onto each other
   C show the way to a food source
   D help other ants cross something

5. *Good* can have the following meanings. Mark the meaning used in paragraph 4.
   A kind
   B benefit
   C skillful
   D pleasant

6. Do you think ant colonies and human society are similar in any way? Tell why or why not.

Who was Frederick Douglass?

1   Frederick Douglass was born as a slave in 1817. He grew up to be a great leader in the fight against slavery.

2   As a child, Frederick learned to read and write a little. But the slave owner beat him and would not allow him to learn more. When he was 21, he made a daring escape. He dressed as a sailor. Using a forged permit, he rode the train north to freedom. He made his home in New York State.

3   Later he published a newspaper to speak out against slavery. He named it *North Star* because escaping slaves followed the North Star at night. People asked him to speak about his life. At first, he felt shy. But he became a famous public speaker. He also wrote a book about his life. During the Civil War, he talked with President Lincoln. He helped convince the president to end slavery.

4   After the Civil War, Frederick Douglass worked to gain civil rights for black citizens. He helped them win the right to vote. For the rest of his life, he inspired black men and women. He once told a group of black students, "What was possible for me is possible for you."

Circle the right answer for questions 1–5. Write your answer to question 6 on a blank piece of paper.

1. When Frederick Douglass was 21, he _____.
   A escaped from slavery
   B published a newspaper
   C learned to read and write
   D became a famous speaker

2. Which word in paragraph 2 means "false and illegal"?
   A forged   C permit
   B daring   D escape

3. Which paragraph tells about ways that Frederick Douglass worked to end slavery?
   A 1   C 3
   B 2   D 4

4. After the Civil War, Frederick Douglass _____.
   A forged a permit
   B fought to end slavery
   C advised President Lincoln
   D helped blacks win the right to vote

5. *Civil* can have the following meanings. Mark the meaning used in paragraph 4.
   A polite   C relating to citizens
   B social   D relating to a court case

6. Think of another African American who was important in the history of the United States. What did he or she do?

How do animals know the way home?

1 A cat named Bobby lived in England. His owner took him to America on an airplane. When the owner returned to England, Bobby was left behind. Yet 13 days later, Bobby arrived at his owner's home. He had crossed an ocean!

2 Animals have a strong sense of where home is and how to get there. Scientists have studied this but still don't really know how it works. Birds travel thousands of miles when the seasons change. Some leave on the exact same day every year. If winter comes too early, the birds may die of the cold. Salmon hatch in fresh water. Then they swim to the ocean. There, they spend most of their lives. When it's time to lay their eggs, though, they always return to the water where they were born.

3 Many animals use the sun or the stars to find their way. Bees' eyes see the tiniest changes in light and dark. So even on a cloudy day, bees follow the sun back to their hive. Some birds use the position of the stars to fly at night.

4 Of course, none of this explains how Bobby found his way home. He didn't fly or swim. He didn't use the sun or the stars. It's clear that animals have senses that people just don't understand.

Circle the right answer for questions 1–5. Write your
answer to question 6 on a blank piece of paper.

1. On cloudy days, bees follow _____ to reach their
   hive.
   A the sun
   B the moon
   C a trail of ants
   D the smell of honey

2. Which word in paragraph 2 means "come out from an egg"?
   A die   C swim
   B lay   D hatch

3. Which paragraph tells what salmon do?
   A 1   C 3
   B 2   D 4

4. If winter comes early, birds may die of cold because _____.
   A the seasons change
   B they lose their feathers
   C they are tired from traveling
   D they leave on the exact same day every year

5. The article does not say, but you can decide that _____.
   A bees have bad eyesight
   B salmon are a kind of fish
   C birds don't fly in the winter
   D animals are afraid of the dark

6. How do you think Bobby found his way home? Write a short story
   to explain what happened to him.

What is a mannequin?

1   Who tries on clothes in a store but never buys any? The answer is a mannequin (MA•nih•kuhn). You've seen mannequins before. They look almost like people. Store workers dress them in the latest clothes. Then they put them in their store windows.

2   You may not know it, but mannequins have been around for a very long time. The oldest one is over 3,500 years old. This wooden mannequin was found in the tomb of an Egyptian king.

3   Since then, mannequins have been made of other things. One hundred years ago, many were made of wax. They had false teeth and glass eyes. But a funny thing happened to these wax "dolls." They melted standing in sunny windows!

4   Later, around 1930, mannequins were made of a special kind of paper. They were lighter and easier to lift and move around than the wooden or wax ones. But these mannequins didn't last long. They would wear out quickly and fall apart.

5   Today, mannequins are made of plastic. They are light and last a long time. So when you go shopping, look at the mannequins, not just their clothes.

Circle the right answer for questions 1–5. Write your answer to question 6 on a blank piece of paper.

1. The article does <u>not</u> tell about _____ mannequins.
   A old
   B wax
   C future
   D today's

2. Which word in paragraph 2 means "place where the dead are put"?
   A tomb   C time
   B years   D king

3. Which paragraph tells what happened to wax mannequins?
   A 1   C 3
   B 2   D 4

4. After they were made of paper, mannequins were made of _____.
   A wax
   B steel
   C wood
   D plastic

5. The article does not say, but you can decide that mannequins _____.
   A are only for women's clothes
   B have changed over time
   C frighten shoppers
   D don't last long

6. The oldest mannequin known about is 3,500 years old. What do you think mannequins will look like 3,500 years from now? What makes you think so?

How can people save water?

1. People cannot live without water. They drink it. They cook with it. They wash their bodies and clothes with it. They water farms and gardens with it.

2. You may think there is plenty of water on Earth. But finding it is getting harder all the time. A lot of water is polluted with waste from factories and homes. And there are more people on Earth now than ever before. So there's less water to go around.

3. That's why it's important to save water whenever you can. Here are a few ideas. Leave the water off while you brush your teeth. Take quick showers instead of baths. If you do take a bath, don't fill the tub too full. Use just enough water and no more.

4. You can also save water in another way. Make sure you don't pollute it. Never throw garbage into a pond, lake, or stream. And if you see someone polluting or wasting, tell a grown-up about it. If people all work together to save water, Earth can be sure of having enough in years to come.

Circle the right answer for questions 1–5. Write your answer to question 6 on a blank piece of paper.

1. The article does <u>not</u> tell about _____.

   A water from oceans

   B how to fill a bathtub

   C what water is used for

   D how water gets polluted

2. Which word in paragraph 2 means "dirty, or not pure"?

   A harder   **C** plenty

   B polluted   **D** waste

3. Which paragraph tells about saving water at home?

   A 1   **C** 3

   B 2   **D** 4

4. Which of these is <u>not</u> a way to save water?

   A Don't throw garbage into a lake.

   B Take quick showers instead of baths.

   C Leave the water off when you brush your teeth.

   D Wash your car at home rather than at a carwash.

5. The article does not say, but you can decide that _____.

   A most people take baths

   B one person can't help to conserve water

   C throwing trash in a pond doesn't hurt anything

   D factories need to be careful where they dump waste

6. What other ways to save water can you think of? Make a list. Then tell which way you think is most important.

What art has lasted for 25,000 years?

1. Australia is an island continent. For thousands of years, its people met no one from the outside world. So their way of life hardly changed during that time. The native Australians hunted for food. When all the food in a place was used, they moved on. Wherever the people went, they took their stories and their art with them.

2. Today, art that is 25,000 years old can still be seen on rock walls in Australia. Some paintings tell stories of the native Australians' everyday life. There are wonderful pictures of kangaroo hunts. Other paintings show spirit beings. These were from the early people's "dreamtime" stories. They tell of a time before there were people. Dreamtime myths and paintings reminded the early Australians of their beliefs. Their main belief was that they were a part of nature.

3. The ancient Australian art has a look all its own. Animals and people don't look real. They're not supposed to. Some paintings were done by great artists. Others were not. Today, there are still a few native Australian artists who paint dreamtime myths. Through them, the ancient art will live on.

Circle the right answer for questions 1–5. Write your answer to question 6 on a blank piece of paper.

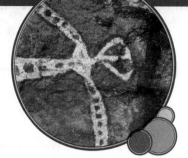

1. Early Australians believed that they _____.
   A should not travel
   B could dream in color
   C were a part of nature
   D would always have good hunting

2. Which word in paragraph 2 means "stories about heroes"?
   A myths
   B beliefs
   C pictures
   D paintings

3. Native Australians changed areas when _____.
   A the weather changed
   B all the food was used
   C the spirits scared them away
   D they were looking for rock walls

4. The article does not say, but you can decide that native Australians _____.
   A ate kangaroo
   B wrote stories in books
   C made realistic paintings
   D did not like nature

5. *Outside* can have the following meanings. Mark the meaning used in paragraph 1.
   A barely possible
   B not included in a group
   C being from another place
   D being on the outer surface

6. Think about things that mean a lot to you. Draw a picture to show some of the most important things in your life. Then write a paragraph to explain your picture.

1   Musk oxen are often called the "Bearded Ones." The animals have long, brown hair hanging down to their feet. They are about the size of cows. But musk oxen don't belong to the ox family. They belong to the goat family. They live in Alaska, Greenland, and Canada.

2   When frightened, musk oxen make a circle. They stand shoulder to shoulder. Then they put their heads down to face the enemy. Their white horns curve down, out, and up. They end in sharp points. The animals look very fierce.

3   For years, people killed many musk oxen for food and wool. Then steps were taken to save the wild animals. Some people even began to raise a few musk oxen. They wanted to use the animals' long silky undercoat. One pound of this silky hair makes six miles of fine wool yarn. The wool can be dyed and made into warm clothes.

4   Musk oxen raised on farms are friendly and like to play. If someone comes to take their picture, they may walk over and put a wet nose on the camera. The hairy animals seem to like their life on the farm.

Circle the right answer for questions 1–5. Write your answer to question 6 on a blank piece of paper.

1. The article does <u>not</u> tell about the _____ of musk oxen.
   A   size   C   color
   B   wool   D   babies

2. Which word in paragraph 3 means "given a different color"?
   A   dyed   C   raise
   B   killed   D   pound

3. Which paragraph tells about where musk oxen can be found?
   A   1   C   3
   B   2   D   4

4. What do musk oxen <u>not</u> do when they are frightened by another animal?
   A   make a circle
   B   put their heads down
   C   stand on their hind legs
   D   stand shoulder to shoulder

5. The article does not say, but you can decide that steps were taken to save musk oxen mostly because _____.
   A   they were popular in zoos
   B   too many were being killed
   C   more were needed for farming
   D   people in other countries wanted them

6. When might be the best time to clip a musk ox's undercoat? Why?

1 The first person to reach the North Pole was Robert E. Peary. Peary made the trip by sled in 1909. But he didn't go alone. An African American named Matthew Henson and four Inuit guides went with him.

2 In 1978, Naomi Uemura of Japan went to the North Pole, too. But Uemura went alone. He had only his sled dogs for company.

3 Uemura's trip was exciting. It was also dangerous. Soon after Uemura started, he was attacked by a huge polar bear. The bear tore apart Uemura's tent and ate all the dog food. Finally, the explorer was able to shoot and kill it. Uemura and the dogs ate fresh bear meat for the next few days.

4 The trip was lonely. Snow stretched as far as the eye could see. There was no one to talk to. It was also very cold, about 50° below zero. Uemura kept a diary. He planned to write a book about the trip when he got back.

5 At last the long trip ended. After 500 miles and many days, Naomi Uemura reached the North Pole. He became the first and only person to do it alone.

Circle the right answer for questions 1–5. Write your answer to question 6 on a blank piece of paper.

1. The first person to reach the North Pole was _____.
   - **A** Naomi Uemura
   - **B** Robert E. Peary
   - **C** Matthew Henson
   - **D** Christopher Columbus

2. Which word in paragraph 4 means "a book you write in every day"?
   - **A** trip
   - **B** zero
   - **C** snow
   - **D** diary

3. Which paragraph tells how Naomi Uemura fought a bear?
   - **A** 1
   - **B** 2
   - **C** 3
   - **D** 4

4. Naomi Uemura's dogs ate fresh bear meat instead of dog food because _____.
   - **A** they liked that food better than dog food
   - **B** Uemura killed many bears along the trip
   - **C** a polar bear ate their dog food and was killed
   - **D** Uemura ate their dog food and then shot a bear

5. The article does not say, but you can decide that _____.
   - **A** sled dogs can't run in cold weather
   - **B** a polar bear provides lots of meat
   - **C** Naomi Uemura lived in an igloo
   - **D** a polar bear only eats meat

6. Would you want to take a trip to the North Pole the same way that Naomi Uemura did? Why or why not?

Why is the baobab tree special?

1   The baobab (BOW•bab) tree looks as if it is growing upside down. Its trunk is bare. Near its top, crooked branches spread out like roots. An old story says that angry gods turned the tree upside down. But it is hard to guess why anyone would be angry at this useful tree.

2   Baobab trees grow in Africa on the edges of the desert. Some grow as tall as a six-story building. They can live as long as 1,000 years. A fruit called monkey bread hangs from the branches of the baobabs. It is about a foot long. Monkey bread is good to eat. It can also be made into a drink. Baobab leaves are used for medicine. The bark can be made into paper, cloth, or rope.

3   All these uses should be enough for any tree. But the baobab has another secret. In a dry land, the baobab can pull in and hold 1,000 gallons of water. It stores the water in its branches. Thirsty people tap the branches to drink. No wonder the baobab is also called the bottle tree. Whatever its name, the baobab is a real friend to people.

Circle the right answer for questions 1–5. Write your answer to question 6 on a blank piece of paper.

1. The article does <u>not</u> tell about the _____ of the baobab tree.
   A bark
   B fruit
   C seeds
   D leaves

2. Which word in paragraph 2 means "sides, or borders"?
   A years
   B edges
   C leaves
   D branches

3. The baobab is called the bottle tree because _____.
   A it stores water in its branches
   B it leaks water from its trunk
   C its branches are crooked
   D it is shaped like a bottle

4. The article does not say, but you can decide that the baobab tree _____.
   A looks like any other tree
   C cannot live in harsh conditions
   B is most useful in the desert
   D is most useful in the mountains

5. *Tap* can have the following meanings. Mark the meaning used in paragraph 3.
   A to select
   B to strike lightly
   C to walk with light steps
   D to cause to flow by piercing

6. Many folktales tell why something happened or how something came to be. Write a short tale that tells how the baobab came to look the way it does.

What is Space Camp?

1   Have you ever wanted to be an astronaut? You can find out what it's like right now. Just go to the United States Space Camp in Huntsville, Alabama. There you can explore the fun and hard work of space travel.

2   Each summer, girls and boys ages 9 to 11 from across the United States and around the world go to Space Camp. They spend six days learning and doing the jobs of real astronauts in space. Each day begins at 6 A.M. During the day, campers see films and hear scientists talk about space. They also watch rockets being built and they examine real spacecraft.

3   Space Campers wear suits just like the astronauts'—only smaller. They eat astronaut food. And they learn how to walk and move around in space. The camp day ends at 9:30 P.M. By that time, campers are ready for sleep.

4   At the end of six days, Space Campers take a pretend space shuttle flight. They use machines like those in the shuttle. They face the same problems and feel the same way as real astronauts. When Space Camp ends, boys and girls are proud to have learned and done so much. They are one step closer to reaching the stars!

Circle the right answer for questions 1–5. Write your answer to question 6 on a blank piece of paper.

1. The article does <u>not</u> tell about _____.
   A floating in space
   B the food campers eat
   C what campers do each day
   D the season Space Camp is open

2. Which word in paragraph 2 means "look at carefully, or check"?
   A doing   C spend
   B hear   D examine

3. Which paragraph tells what happens at the end of Space Camp?
   A 1   C 3
   B 2   D 4

4. The article does not say, but you can decide that campers _____.
   A don't like astronaut food
   B put in a long day at Space Camp
   C spend all their time in a spacecraft
   D help astronauts solve problems on the shuttle

5. *Face* can have the following meanings. Mark the meaning used in paragraph 4.
   A deal with
   B outer surface
   C meet in competition
   D front part of the head

6. Would you like to be an astronaut and travel and work in space? Why or why not?

What is the mystery of the monarch?

1   Monarchs (MAHN•arks) are beautiful butterflies. Their wings are orange and black with white spots on them. In the summer, monarchs live in many places. But somehow they know that they must leave when the weather gets cold. Winter's frost will kill them. So each fall, monarchs fly south. Then each spring, they fly north again, laying eggs along the way.

2   The butterflies go back to the same place every fall. Some travel for weeks to get there. Many fly more than a thousand miles. They travel in large groups. Sometimes they look like a gold ribbon stretching across the sky. Monarchs live less than a year. So there are no old ones to lead the way to warmer places. People don't understand how the young monarchs know where to go. This is the mystery of the monarch.

3   One place these butterflies go is in California. It is known as "Butterfly Town, U.S.A." The monarchs even return to the same trees there year after year. People in the town love the insects. They have a parade to welcome them each fall. And city laws protect the monarchs. Everyone wants them to keep coming back.

Circle the right answer for questions 1–5. Write your answer to question 6 on a blank piece of paper.

1. "Butterfly Town, U.S.A.," is in _____.
   A Hawaii
   B Florida
   C California
   D New York

2. Which word in paragraph 3 means "go back"?
   A welcome   C return
   B protect   D love

3. Young monarchs must know where to go when they travel because _____.
   A the older butterflies live less than a year
   B they fly ahead of the older butterflies
   C the older butterflies travel separately
   D they carry the older butterflies

4. What do monarchs do in the summer before they fly south in the fall?
   A They fly north.
   B They travel alone.
   C They all go to California.
   D They live in many places.

5. The article does not say, but you can decide that monarchs _____.
   A travel alone
   B fly across oceans
   C move only in the fall
   D lay eggs in many different places

6. How do you think city laws can protect the monarch butterflies?

What is a neighborhood island?

1   There are hundreds of islands on Earth. But only 200 of these are really important islands. One of the smallest important islands is called Manhattan.

2   Manhattan Island is $2\frac{1}{2}$ miles wide and $13\frac{1}{2}$ miles long. It is known for its many beautiful tall buildings. But they are not the most interesting things on this island. The neighborhoods on Manhattan Island are really special.

3   Many immigrants (IM•ih•grents) live there. Immigrants are people who move to the United States from other countries. They bring many skills and experiences with them to their new home.

4   Think of a neighborhood on Manhattan Island. In this neighborhood, there are people from Puerto Rico running a bakery. Next door, Koreans have a vegetable stand. On the same block, East Indians sell candy and newspapers. Cubans run a restaurant. And across the street, Russians open a clothing store.

5   Each group of immigrants is different. They have their own languages, foods, and ways of doing things. Together the immigrants are like squares in a quilt. Manhattan has many of these interesting neighborhoods. It really is a neighborhood island.

Circle the right answer for questions 1–5. Write your answer to question 6 on a blank piece of paper.

1. The article does <u>not</u> tell about _____.
   - **A** how big Manhattan is
   - **B** a neighborhood on Manhattan Island
   - **C** what immigrants might do for a living
   - **D** how many tall buildings are on Manhattan Island

2. Which word in paragraph 3 means "talents to do jobs"?
   - **A** countries
   - **B** immigrants
   - **C** skills
   - **D** experiences

3. Which paragraph tells how many islands there are on Earth?
   - **A** 1
   - **B** 2
   - **C** 3
   - **D** 4

4. In Manhattan, people can get food from almost any country in the world mostly because _____.
   - **A** many immigrants have settled there
   - **B** people there speak many languages
   - **C** the island has many tall buildings
   - **D** the island is so small

5. The article does not say, but you can decide that Manhattan _____.
   - **A** is difficult to get to
   - **B** is quiet on most days
   - **C** doesn't allow immigrants to open businesses
   - **D** has more interesting neighborhoods than most islands

6. Imagine you were telling a visitor from another country about your neighborhood. Write a description of it. Tell about the people, buildings, shops, and parks. Then tell about why you like living there.

1   Pretend that you are in Alaska. It is a clear, dark night. You see a greenish glow overhead. Ribbons of green and red light drift across the sky. Then the lights ripple like curtains blowing in the wind. What are you seeing? You are seeing the northern lights.

2   The northern lights are most often seen near the North and South Poles. To understand why, you need to know about the Earth's magnetic field. You have probably seen a magnet attract metal objects. Earth itself is like a magnet. Its magnetic field is strongest near the North and South Poles. It attracts bits of electrically charged matter called particles. The particles are too small to see.

3   These particles come from the sun. The sun is a ball of burning gases. These gases explode and throw particles toward Earth. The Earth's magnetic field draws the particles toward the North and South Poles. Here the particles hit gases high in the Earth's atmosphere. These collisions release light. And people call this light the northern lights.

4   Someday maybe you will see the northern lights. Enjoy the show! And think about the amazing process that creates it.

Circle the right answer for questions 1–5. Write your answer to question 6 on a blank piece of paper.

1. The Earth's magnetic field attracts _____.
   A particles from the sun
   B balls of burning gas
   C ribbons of light
   D gases in the air

2. Which word in paragraph 1 means "move in a slow, smooth way"?
   A glow   C across
   B drift   D blowing

3. This article tells mostly about _____ the northern lights.
   A where people can see   C why people like
   B the best time to see   D what causes

4. After particles from the sun hit gases in the Earth's atmosphere, _____.
   A light is released
   B the gases explode
   C the Earth gets hotter
   D metal becomes magnetic

5. *Draws* can have the following meanings. Mark the meaning used in paragraph 3.
   A makes a line
   B removes liquid from
   C allows air to pass through
   D pulls in a certain direction

6. Think about a time you played with a magnet. Tell what you noticed about the way the magnet worked.

Who was Jim Henson?

1   "It's not easy being green." These are the words of a puppet named Kermit the Frog. Kermit is known and loved by fans around the world. Jim Henson was the creator of Kermit and many other puppets. Henson has been called one of the top artists and entertainers of the 20th century.

2   Jim's interest in puppets began early. In high school, he made puppets for a TV show for kids. In college, he made a short TV puppet show called *Sam and Friends.* This show included the first version of Kermit. In 1963 he invented the Muppets. Frank Oz became Jim's partner. Frank was the voice of Miss Piggy. The Muppets appeared in a number of TV shows and movies.

3   In 1969, Jim's puppets joined a new TV show for children. It was called *Sesame Street.* Bert and Ernie, Big Bird, Grover, and Cookie Monster were a huge success. The show has been on the air for more than 35 years. It is watched in many countries.

4   Jim Henson died in 1990. Friends say he was a kind, patient man. His friend Frank Oz said, "Jim was never wimpy. He had a strength to his sweetness."

Circle the right answer for questions 1–5. Write your answer to question 6 on a blank piece of paper.

1. Jim Henson created the first version of Kermit when Jim _____.
   A worked for *Sesame Street*
   B invented the Muppets
   C was in high school
   D was in college

2. Which word in paragraph 4 means "able to wait calmly"?
   A kind   C strength
   B patient   D sweetness

3. Which paragraph tells about Jim Henson's personality?
   A 1   C 3
   B 2   D 4

4. Frank Oz became Jim's partner before Jim _____.
   A worked for *Sesame Street*
   B created *Sam and Friends*
   C invented the Muppets
   D developed Kermit

5. The article does not say, but you can decide that Jim Henson _____.
   A did the voices of all the puppets
   B liked movies more than TV
   C was a creative person
   D was timid and shy

6. Tell about a puppet that you have seen and enjoyed. What do you like about the puppet?